Maisy at the Beach
Sticker Book

Lucy Cousins

Take the sticker pages out of the middle of this book.
Open the pages so the stickers and the pictures
in the book can be seen side by side.
Read the words on each page.
Children can choose which sticker to peel off
and where to put it in each picture.

WALKER BOOKS
AND SUBSIDIARIES
LONDON · BOSTON · SYDNEY · AUCKLAND

Maisy and her friends are at the beach.

Can you put on their sunhats?

Eddie goes paddling. What else is in the water?

What a
sunny day!
Help Maisy
look for seashells
in the sand.

Find Cyril's spade and help him build some sandcastles.

Catch the beach-ball, Tallulah!

Find Panda and put him under the palm-tree.

Eddie and Charley sail their toy boats.

Charley needs his rubber ring.

Cyril and Maisy buy ice creams.

Find an umbrella for the ice-cream cart.

What a lovely day
at the seaside.
Bye-bye, Maisy.